Alleluya!

77 songs for thinking people
chosen by David Gadsby and John Hoggarth

WORDS EDITION
with drawings by David McKee

A & C Black · London

Published by A. & C. Black (Publishers) Ltd 35 Bedford Row London WC1R 4JH
© 1980 A. & C. Black (Publishers) Ltd
Reprinted 1981, 1983, 1985, 1989

ISBN 0 7136 2000 5
Printed in Great Britain by Hollen Street Press Limited, Slough, Berkshire

Contents

1 Hey, now, everybody sing!

Hey, now, everybody sing,
Everybody sing to the Lord our God;
Hey, now, everybody sing,
Everybody sing to the Lord our God.

Everybody join in a song of praise,
Come along and sing with me;
Glory, Alleluya,
Glory, Alleluya,
I'm so glad I'm free.

Hey, now, everybody sing,
Everybody sing to the Lord our God;
Hey, now, everybody sing,
Everybody sing to the Lord our God.
Everybody sing, everybody sing,
Everybody sing to the Lord our God:
Everybody sing, everybody sing,
Everybody sing to the Lord our God.
Everybody sing!

Orien Johnson

2 God loves a cheerful giver

God loves a cheerful giver;
Give it all you've got.
He loves to hear you laughing
When you're in an awkward spot.
When the odds add up against you,
It's time to stop and sing:
"Praise God!" To praise him is
A joyous thing.

1   Peter always made a fuss;
Peter was impetuous.
He knew hard times
When he denied his Lord.
But hardly had he fallen when
He got right up, began again.
Christ named him his successor
As his reward.
     God loves a cheerful giver . . .

2   Jonah was a gloomy sort;
He always had a sad report.
He ran from God,
He ran and he set sail.
His journey's end was quite abrupt,
A fish came by and swallowed him up.
He spent three dark and dreary days
Inside the whale.
     God loves a cheerful giver . . .

3   Holy Job was richly blessed;
    He lost it all but stood the test.
    For Job was steadfast
    In his misery.
    "God gives to me, he takes away.
    Blessed be the name of God this day."
    And he was doubly blessed
    For his fidelity.
        God loves a cheerful giver . . .

Sr. Miriam Therese Winter

3 Sing Hosanna!

1   Give me joy in my heart, keep me praising,
    Give me joy in my heart, I pray;
    Give me joy in my heart, keep me praising,
    Keep me praising 'til the break of day:

        Sing Hosanna! Sing Hosanna!
        Sing Hosanna to the King of Kings!
        Sing Hosanna! Sing Hosanna!
        Sing Hosanna to the King!

2   Give me peace in my heart, keep me resting . . .

3   Give me love in my heart, keep me serving . . .

Traditional

4 The Lord's Day

1   This is the day,
    This is the day that the Lord has made,
        that the Lord has made.
    We will rejoice,
    We will rejoice and be glad in it,
        and be glad in it.
    This is the day that the Lord has made,
    We will rejoice and be glad in it.
    This is the day that the Lord has made.

2   This is the day,
    This is the day when he rose again,
        when he rose again.
    We will rejoice,
    We will rejoice and be glad in it,
        and be glad in it.
    This is the day when he rose again,
    We will rejoice and be glad in it.
    This is the day when he rose again.

3   This is the day,
    This is the day when the Spirit came,
        when the Spirit came.
    We will rejoice,
    We will rejoice and be glad in it,
        and be glad in it.
    This is the day when the Spirit came,
    We will rejoice and be glad in it.
    This is the day when the Spirit came.

Traditional Fijian

5 Happiness is

Happiness is,
Happiness is,
Happiness is,
Different things to different people,
That's what happiness is.

1 To a preacher, it's a prayer, prayer, prayer;
To the Beatles, it's a Yeah! Yeah! Yeah!
To a golfer, it's a hole in one;
To a father, it's a brand new son.
    Happiness is . . .

2 On a desert, it's a drink, drink, drink;
To a show-girl, it's a mink, mink, mink;
To a banker, lots and lots of dough;
To a racer, it's a G.T.O.
    Happiness is . . .

3 To a sailor, it's the sea, sea, sea;
To my mother, why, it's me, me, me;
To the birdies, it's the sky above;
But to my mind, it's the one I love.
    Happiness is . . .

Paul Parnes and Paul Erans

6 Alleluya

1   Let all the people raise
    Their joyful song of praise:
        Alleluya, alleluya!
    Freely now let them sing
    Glory to God the King:
        Alleluya, alleluya!
    Let choirs that dwell on high
    Re-echo through the sky:
        Alleluya, alleluya!
    Saints who in glory dwell
    With joy the chorus swell:
        Alleluya, alleluya, alleluya!
    Singing in Paradise
    To the exalted Christ:
        Alleluya, alleluya!

2   Swift planets on your way;
    Bright constellations say:
        Alleluya, alleluya!
    Sing, clouds that onward sweep;
    Sing, thunder loud and deep:
        Alleluya, alleluya!
    Lightning so wild and bright,
    Floods in his praise unite:
        Alleluya, alleluya!
    Sing, wind and winter snow;
    Sing, sun and summer glow:
        Alleluya, alleluya, alleluya!
    Woodlands that stir in Spring,
    Glorious forests sing:
        Alleluya, alleluya!

3   Birds in your feathers gay,
     Exalt your Lord, and say:
        Alleluya, alleluya!
     Beasts now take up the strain,
     Sing to your Lord again:
        Alleluya, alleluya!
     Let every towering hill,
     Each valley, echo still:
        Alleluya, alleluya!
     Let depths of ocean cry
     And continents reply:
        Alleluya, alleluya, alleluya!
     To God, who all has made,
     This tribute now be paid:
        Alleluya, alleluya!

4   This song the Father loves;
     This anthem Christ approves:
        Alleluya, alleluya!
     Our heart and voice we wake,
     And children answer make:
        Alleluya, alleluya!
     From all be now outpoured
     This chorus to the Lord:
        Alleluya, alleluya!
     Thus, singing evermore,
     We shall our God adore:
        Alleluya, alleluya, alleluya!
     To God, the Three in One,
     Let endless praise be done:
        Alleluya, alleluya!

Robert J. Figures

7 Now let us sing

      Now let us sing;
Sing to the power of the Lord come down.
      Now let us sing;
Sing to the power of the Lord come down.
      Lift up your voice,
Lift up your voice.
      Be not afraid,
Be not afraid.
      Now let us sing.

Sing to the power of the Lord come down.

Traditional

8 Praise to the Lord our God

Praise to the Lord our God, let us sing together,
Lifting our hearts and our voices to sing with
Joy and gladness.
Come along, along, along, and sing with
      praise.

Estelle White

9 You've gotta move

1 You've gotta move when the Spirit says move,
You've gotta move when the Spirit says move,
'Cos when the Spirit says move,
You've gotta move when the Spirit,
Move when the Spirit says move.

2 You've gotta sing . . .

3 You've gotta clap . . .

4 You've gotta shout . . .

5 You've gotta jump . . .

Traditional

10 Magic penny

Love is something if you give it away,
    give it away, give it away.
Love is something if you give it away,
You end up having more.

1   It's just like a magic penny;
   Hold it tight and you won't have any;
   Lend it, spend it, and you'll have so many,
   They'll roll all over the floor, for
       Love is something if you give it away . . .

2   So let's go dancing till the break of day,
   And if there's a piper, we can pay.
   For love is something if you give it away,
   You end up having more.
       Love is something if you give it away . . .

Malvina Reynolds

11 Guantanamera

Guantanamera, guajira Guantanamera,
Guantanamera, guajira Guantanamera.

1 I give my songs to the people,
To those who know how to sing them;
I give my songs to the people,
To those who know how to sing them.
I sing for them in their trouble,
For any help I can bring them.
    Guantanamera, guajira Guantanamera . . .

2 My song is red like the fire,
My song is green as the meadows;
My song is red like the fire,
My song is green as the meadows;
And like the prey of the hunter
It has to lie in the shadows.
    Guantanamera, guajira Guantanamera . . .

3 It is the poor and the lonely
Who need our love and compassion;
It is the poor and the lonely
Who need our love and compassion.
The little streams in the valley
Are more to me than the ocean.
    Guantanamera, guajira Guantanamera . . .

Pronunciation note: guajira—gwa-*he*-ra

José Marti, translated by Geoffrey Brace

12 Forever free

1   Well, I was walkin' along
     Just a-singin' a song
     And a-goin' my way.
     When a lady stopped me and
     She said where ya goin',
     Where ya goin' today.
     Well, I said I'm a-tryin' to
     Discover the time when all
     Folks can find the time to dine.
     Around a table of one,
     No need to run, and I'll
     Tell you why.

        I found a new life
        Forever free.
        A new way that's gonna be me.
        Whatever may come, whatever may go
        In between
        With a love I know.

2 Well, I was sittin' one day,
    Just a-thinkin' away
    Over where I've run.
    And a stranger stopped me
    And he said where you been,
    Where you been, my son.
    Well, I said I been goin'
    To the end of town and a
    Back around, a neighbour I found.
    I can welcome the dawn,
    My fear is gone.
    I am not a clown.

3 Well, I went climbin' a hill
    And the world stood still,
    Oh, I looked and saw
    People standin' together
    And a-knowin' and a-flowin'
    And a-growin' tall.
    Don't wanna be a-dead before
    I die, gonna get on by,
    I'm gonna "fly".
    In the Good Lord's plan,
    It's the way I am.
    I'm gonna be fine.

Yohann Anderson

13 Lullaby for the times

1   On with your shoes, come let me help you,
       Time for school, you mustn't be late;
       Now you look all fresh and shining,
       Hair all tidy, satchel straight.
           Don't you mind the empty chair, love,
           Dad'll be home before too long;
           He sat down and went to jail, love,
           So you could grow up straight and strong.

2   Here's your bus fare, don't you lose it,
       Off you go now, down the lane;
       Don't forget to take your raincoat,
       Sky is cloudy, looks like rain.
           Mind you drink up all your milk, love,
           Just as you do when Dad's at home;
           He sat down and went to jail, love,
           So that the milk won't hurt your bones.

3   Now for a kiss, it's time to run
       If you're to beat that morning bell;
       Tell the teachers if you're late
       Your Dad is in a prison cell.
           Tell them he's there so you can walk
           And run and race and jump and fly;
           Tell them your Dad's in prison so that
           You and the other kids won't die.

Ewan MacColl

14 This little light of mine

This little light of mine, I'm gonna let it shine,
This little light of mine, I'm gonna let it shine,
This little light of mine, I'm gonna let it shine,
Let it shine, let it shine, let it shine.

1   The light that shines is the light of love,
Lights the darkness from above.
It shines on me and it shines on you,
And shows what the power of love can do.
I'm gonna shine my light both far and near,
I'm gonna shine my light both bright and clear.
Where there's a dark corner in this land
I'm gonna let my little light shine.
         This little light of mine . . .

2   On Monday he gave me the gift of love,
Tuesday, peace came from above.
On Wednesday he told me to have more faith,
On Thursday he gave me a little more grace.
Friday, he told me just to watch and pray,
Saturday, he told me just what to say.
On Sunday he gave me the power divine
To let my little light shine.
         This little light of mine . . .

Traditional

15 I watch the sunrise

1   I watch the sunrise lighting the sky,
    Casting its shadows near.
    And on this morning, bright though it be,
    I feel those shadows near me.

        But you are always close to me,
        Following all my ways.
        May I be always close to you,
        Following all your ways, Lord.

2   I watch the sunlight shine through the clouds,
    Warming the earth below.
    And at the midday life seems to say:
    "I feel your brightness near me,"
            For you are always . . .

3   I watch the sunset fading away,
    Lighting the clouds with sleep.
    And as the evening closes its eyes,
    I feel your presence near me.
            For you are always . . .

4   I watch the moonlight guarding the night,
    Waiting till morning comes.
    The air is silent, earth is at rest –
    Only your peace is near me.
            Yes, you are always . . .

John Glynn

16 *Abundantly*

1   From mountains high, cool waters flow,
    The singing breeze, green meadows grow;
    Shine tall pine trees, blue sky above,
    Are all expressions of my Lord's love.
        And this one God who made all these,
        Is interested in you and me;
        His greatest gift is to make us free,
        New self, more life, abundantly.

2   God speaks, he acts, what he says he will,
    His promises he will fulfil;
    Through Christ his focused love appears,
    To put at ease the life that fears.
        Relationships to all he brings,
        The solid feel inside me rings;
        No phoney do I have to be,
        For God, through Christ, accepts just me.

3   The dawning sun, a bright new light,
    For folks to join, no need to fight;
    Creation through variety
    Displays God's plan for unity.
        And this one God who made all these,
        Is interested in you and me;
        His greatest gift is to make us free,
        New self, more life, abundantly.

Yohann Anderson

17 Love is his word

1 Love is his word, love is his way,
   Feasting with men, fasting alone,
   Living and dying, rising again,
   Love, only love, is his way.

      Richer than gold is the love of my Lord,
      Better than splendour or wealth.

2 Love is his way, love is his mark,
   Sharing his last Passover feast,
   Christ at the table, host to the Twelve,
   Love, only love, is his mark.

3 Love is his mark, love is his sign,
   Bread for our strength, wine for our joy,
   "This is my body, this is my blood."
   Love, only love, is his sign.

4 Love is his sign, love is his news,
   "Do this," he said, "lest you forget
   All my deep sorrow, all my dear blood."
   Love, only love, is his news.

5 Love is his news, love is his name,
   We are his own, chosen and called,
   Family, brethren, cousins and kin,
   Love, only love, is his name.

6 Love is his name, love is his law.
Hear his command, all who are his:
"Love one another, I have loved you."
Love, only love, is his law.

7 Love is his law, love is his word:
Love of the Lord, Father and Word,
Love of the Spirit, God ever one.
Love, only love, is his word.

Luke Connaughton

18 Kol dōdi

Kol dōdi, kol dōdi, kol dōdi hiné ze ba,
Kol dōdi, kol dōdi, kol dōdi hiné ze ba.
M'dalég al heharim m'kapéts al hag'vaōt,
M'dalég al heharim m'kapéts al hag'vaōt.

Hark! my beloved, behold he cometh,
Leaping upon the mountains,
Skipping upon the hills.

Song of Songs 2, v.8

19 Music of the world a-turnin'

I hear the music of the world a-turnin',
Can't you hear the sweet sounds of the world
    a-turnin'?
Stop, look and listen, you can hear things a-growin',
You can have music wherever you go.

1   I hear the music of the world a-turnin':
There are some folks laughin', there are some
    folks cryin',
Kids playin' in the streets sound sweeter than a choir,
All you gotta do is listen
    to hear the music of the world a-turnin'...

2   I hear the symphony of the traffic in the city:
There are horns a-blowin', there are heels a-clickin',
Ash cans a-rattlin' as the sun begins to rise,
All you gotta do is listen
    to hear the music of the world a-turnin'...

3   The wind writes a special song for each and every day:
It's got the rain a-dancin', and the thunder
    a-clappin'.
Don't just ignore it, there's a concert all around you,
All you gotta do is listen
    to hear the music of the world a-turnin'...

Estelle Levitt and Don Thomas

20 Nowhere Man

He's a real Nowhere Man,
Sitting in his nowhere land,
Making all his nowhere plans for nobody.

Doesn't have a point of view,
Knows not where he's going to.
Isn't he a bit like you and me ?

Nowhere Man, please listen,
You don't know what you're missing.
Nowhere Man, the world is at your command !

He's as blind as he can be,
Just sees what he wants to see.
Nowhere Man, can you see me at all ?

Nowhere Man, don't worry,
Take your time, don't hurry.
Leave it all till somebody else lends you a hand.

He's a real Nowhere Man,
Sitting in his nowhere land,
Making all his nowhere plans for nobody,
Making all his nowhere plans for nobody,
Making all his nowhere plans for nobody.

John Lennon and Paul McCartney

21 The games people play

1   Oh, the games people play, now,
      Every night and every day, now.
      Never meanin' what they say, now.
      Never sayin' what they mean.
      And they while away the hours
      In their ivory towers,
      'Til they're covered up with flowers,
      In the back of a black limousine.

            La, da, da, da, da, da, da,
            La, da, da, da, da, da, dee.
            Talkin' 'bout you and me,
            And the games people play.

2   Oh, we make one another cry;
      Break a heart, then say good-bye.
      Cross our heart and hope to die,
      That the other was to blame.
      Neither one will ever give in.
      So, we gaze at an eight by ten,
      Thinkin' 'bout the things that might have been,
      It's a dirty rotten shame.

3   People walkin' up to you,
      Singin' Glory Hallelujah!
      And they're tryin' to sock it to you
      In the name of the Lord.
      They're gonna teach you how to meditate;
      Read your horoscope, cheat your fate,
      And furthermore to hell with hate,
      Come on, get on board.

4   Look around, tell me what you see,
    What's happenin' to you and me?
    God grant me the serenity,
    To remember who I am.
    'Cause you're givin' up your sanity
    For your pride and your vanity.
    Turn your back on humanity.
    And you don't give a da, da, da, da, da.

Joe South

22 Little boxes

1   Little boxes on the hillside,
    Little boxes made of ticky tacky;
    Little boxes on the hillside,
    Little boxes all the same.
        There's a green one, and a pink one,
        And a blue one, and a yellow one;
        And they're all made out of ticky tacky,
        And they all look just the same.

2   And the people in the houses,
    All went to the university;
    Where they were put in boxes,
    And they came out all the same.
        And there's doctors, and there's lawyers,
        And business executives;
        And they're all made out of ticky tacky,
        And they all look just the same.

3   And they all play on the golf course,
    And drink their martinis dry;
    And they all have pretty children,
    And the children go to school,
        And the children go to summer camp,
        And then to the university;
        Where they are put in boxes,
        And they come out all the same.

4   And the boys go into business,
    And marry and raise a family;
    And they all get put in boxes,
    Little boxes all the same.
        There's a green one, and a pink one,
        And a blue one, and a yellow one;
        And they're all made out of ticky tacky,
        And they all look just the same.

Malvina Reynolds

23 Bus story

No one talks to anyone in buses,
No one seems to have a thing to say –
Look at all the people sitting there like statues,
Trying to hide behind their disguises for the day.

1 Now, lady, please move over and I'll sit down next
        to you;
   I'd like to know you better, can you spare a word
        or two?
   We've not got much time together,
   So let's put it to good use,
   And it doesn't have to matter
   That we've not been introduced. But
        No one talks to anyone . . .

2 We could joke about the weather, we could chat
        about the kids,
   But you've got a wet umbrella, and it's poking in
        my ribs.
   Perhaps I'd better read my paper –
   Now she's staring into space,
   And we're fully paid up members
   Of the great commuter race. And
        No one talks to anyone . . .

3   I feel that I'm a failure, though I hope it doesn't
       show;
   I tried to love my neighbour, but on buses it's no go;
   So it's farewell and forever,
   Ring the bell and off I crawl;
   That's another journey over
   And we haven't moved at all.

Leon Rosselson

24 Rain and sun

Rain falling, sun shining,
Rain falling, sun shining,
The Devil and his wife
Behind the church fighting.

    Rain falling, sun shining,
    Rain falling, sun shining,
    Rain falling, sun shining,

Rain falling, sun shining,
The Devil and his wife
Behind the church fighting.

Odette Thomas

25 This train is bound for glory

1   This train is bound for glory, this train.
    This train is bound for glory, this train.
    This train is bound for glory,
    Don't ride none but the righteous and holy,
    This train is bound for glory, this train.

2   This train don't carry no gamblers, this train.
    This train don't carry no gamblers, this train.
    This train don't carry no gamblers,
    Robbers, thieves or big shot ramblers,
    This train is bound for glory, this train.

3   This train don't carry no liars, this train.
    This train don't carry no liars, this train.
    This train don't carry no liars,
    Cheats or hypocrites or high flyers,
    This train is bound for glory, this train.

Spiritual

26 Silver trumpet

1 Well, I've never been to Heaven, but I've been told,
    Hand me down my silver trumpet, Gabriel;
The gates are made of pearl and the streets are
    made of gold,
    Hand me down my silver trumpet, Lord.

    O hand me down, O hand me down,
    O hand me down my silver trumpet, Gabriel.
    Send it down, hand it down,
    Any ol' way, just get it down!
    Hand me down my silver trumpet, Lord.

2 If religion were a thing that money could buy,
    Hand me down my silver trumpet, Gabriel;
The rich would live and the poor would die,
    Hand me down my silver trumpet, Lord.

3 Well now, if you want a silver trumpet like mine,
    Hand me down my silver trumpet, Gabriel;
You'd better learn to play it in plenty of time,
    Hand me down my silver trumpet, Lord.

Spiritual

27 I'm on my way

1 I'm on my way to Freedom Land,
   I'm on my way to Freedom Land,
   I'm on my way to Freedom Land,
   I'm on my way, Great God, I'm on my way.

2 I asked my sister to come with me . . .

3 I asked my brother to come with me . . .

4 I asked my boss to let me go . . .

5 If he says no, I'll go anyhow . . .

Spiritual

28 We are crossing Jordan River

1 We are crossing that Jordan River,
Want my crown, I want my crown!
We are crossing that Jordan River,
I want my crown, my golden crown!
> Jordan River, deep and wide,
> I got a home on the other side.
> Oh, we are crossing that Jordan River,
> I want my crown, I want my crown!

2 Now, when I get to Heaven,
I'm gonna sit down on that golden throne.
Now, when I get to Heaven,
I'm gonna sit down on that golden throne.
> Jordan River, chilly and cold,
> Chills the body but not the soul.
> We are crossing that Jordan River,
> I want my crown, I want my crown!

3 We are climbing Jacob's ladder,
I want to sit down on that golden throne.
We are climbing Jacob's ladder,
I want to sit down on that golden throne.
> Jordan River, deep and wide,
> I got a home on the other side.
> We are crossing that Jordan River,
> I want my crown, I want my crown!

> *Repeat the first verse*

Spiritual

29 Twelve gates to the city

Oh, what a beautiful city,
Oh, what a beautiful city,
Oh, what a beautiful city, well,
Twelve gates into the city,
    Allelu.

1   Three gates into the east,
Three gates into the west,
Three gates into the north,
Three gates into the south, making that
Twelve gates into the city,
    Allelu.
    Well, oh what a beautiful city . . .

2   See those children yonder,
They all dressed in red,
They must be the children,
Children that Moses led. You know, there're
Twelve gates into the city,
    Allelu.
    Well, oh what a beautiful city . . .

3   When I get to Heaven,
I'm going to sing and shout,
There ain't nobody up there
Who's going to put me out. You know, there're
Twelve gates into the city,
    Allelu.
    Well, oh what a beautiful city . . .

Spiritual

30 When I'm on my journey

1 When I'm on my journey, don't you weep after me,
When I'm on my journey, don't you weep after me,
When I'm on my journey, don't you weep after me,
    I don't want you to weep after me.

2 Every lonely river must go home to the sea,
Every lonely river must go home to the sea,
Every lonely river must go home to the sea,
    I don't want you to weep after me.

3 When the stars are falling and the thunder starts
    to roll,
When the stars are falling and the thunder starts
    to roll,
When the stars are falling and the thunder starts
    to roll,
    I don't want you to weep after me.

4 High up on the mountain, leave my sorrow down
    below,
High up on the mountain, leave my sorrow down
    below,
High up on the mountain, leave my sorrow down
    below,
    I don't want you to weep after me.

Spiritual

31 Blowin' in the wind

1 How many roads must a man walk down
      before you call him a man ?
  Yes, 'n' how many seas must a white dove sail
      before she sleeps in the sand ?
  Yes, 'n' how many times must the cannon balls fly
      before they're forever banned ?

    The answer, my friend, is blowin' in the wind,
    The answer is blowin' in the wind.

2 How many times must a man look up
      before he can see the sky ?
  Yes, 'n' how many ears must one man have
      before he can hear people cry ?
  Yes, 'n' how many deaths will it take till he knows
      that too many people have died ?

3 How many years can a mountain exist
      before it's washed to the sea ?
  Yes, 'n' how many years can some people exist
      before they're allowed to be free ?
  Yes, 'n' how many times can a man turn his head
      pretending he just doesn't see ?

Bob Dylan

32 Turn, turn, turn

To everything, turn, turn, turn,
There is a season, turn, turn, turn,
And a time for every purpose under heaven.

1 A time to be born, a time to die;
A time to plant, a time to reap;
A time to kill, a time to heal;
A time to laugh, a time to weep.
        To everything, turn . . .

2 A time to build up, a time to break down;
A time to dance, a time to mourn;
A time to cast away stones,
A time to gather stones together.
        To everything, turn . . .

3 A time of love, a time of hate;
A time of war, a time of peace;
A time you may embrace,
A time to refrain from embracing.
        To everything, turn . . .

4 A time to gain, a time to lose;
A time to rend, a time to sew;
A time to love, a time to hate;
A time of peace, I swear it's not too late.
        To everything, turn . . .

Adapted from Ecclesiastes 3, vv.1-8 by Pete Seeger

33 Both sides now

1   Bows and flows of angel hair,
    And ice-cream castles in the air,
    And feather canyons everywhere:
    I've looked at clouds that way.
    But now they only block the sun;
    They rain and snow on everyone.
    So many things I would have done,
    But clouds got in my way.
            I've looked at clouds from both sides now,
            From up and down and still somehow
            It's clouds' illusions I recall:
            I really don't know clouds at all.

2   Moons and Junes and ferris wheels,
    The dizzy dancing way you feel,
    As every fairy-tale comes real:
    I've looked at love that way.
    But now it's just another show;
    You leave them laughing when you go.
    And if you care, don't let them know,
    Don't give yourself away.
            I've looked at love from both sides now,
            From give and take and still somehow
            It's love's illusions I recall:
            I really don't know love at all.

3   Tears and fears and feeling proud
    To say "I love you" right out loud,
    Dreams and schemes and circus crowds:
    I've looked at life that way.
    But now, old friends are acting strange;
    They shake their heads, they say I've changed.
    But something's lost, but something's gained
    In living every day.
        I've looked at life from both sides now,
        From win and lose and still somehow
        It's life's illusions I recall:
        I really don't know life at all.

Joni Mitchell

34 Can't help but wonder

1 It's a long and dusty road,
It's a hot and a heavy load,
And the folks I meet ain't always kind.
Some are bad and some are good,
Some have done the best they could,
Some have tried to ease my troublin' mind.

> And I can't help but wonder where I'm bound,
> where I'm bound,
> Can't help but wonder where I'm bound.

2 I have wandered through this land
Just a-doin' the best I can,
Tryin' to find what I was meant to do.
And the people that I see
Look as worried as can be,
And it looks like they are wonderin', too.

3 I had a little girl one time,
She had lips like sherry wine
And she loved me till my head went plumb insane,
But I was too blind to see
She was driftin' away from me,
And my good gal went off on the morning train.

4 And I had a buddy back home,
But he started out to roam,
And I hear he's out by Frisco Bay.
And sometimes when I've had a few
His old voice comes singin' through,
And I'm goin' out to see him some old day.

5   If you see me passing by
    And you sit and you wonder why,
    And you wish that you were a rambler too,
    Nail your shoes to the kitchen floor,
    Lace 'em up and bar the door,
    Thank your stars for the roof that's over you.

Tom Paxton

35 What have they done to the rain?

1   Just a little rain falling all around,
    The grass lifts its head to the heavenly sound,
    Just a little rain, just a little rain,
    What have they done to the rain ?

            Just a little boy standing in the rain,
            The gentle rain that falls for years,
            And the grass is gone, the boy disappears,
            And rain keeps falling like helpless tears,
            And what have they done to the rain ?

2   Just a little breeze out of the sky,
    The leaves nod their heads as the breeze blows by,
    Just a little breeze with some smoke in its eye,
    What have they done to the rain ?

Malvina Reynolds

36 Where have the seals gone?

1   Where have the seals gone ? Where are the whales
    That once used our waters before there were sails ?
    Where are the emus that once used to roam
    The fields and the forests we've turned into home ?

        They've all gone away as the sun turns to rain.
        I live here and wonder will they ever
        Come again, come again, come again ?

2   Where have the seals gone ? Where are the whales
    That once used our waters before there were sails ?
    Where are the people who lived here before
    And how is it, tell me, they're not here any more ?

Brian Fitzgerald

37 Where have all the flowers gone?

1   Where have all the flowers gone ?
      Long time passing.
  Where have all the flowers gone ?
      Long time ago.
  Where have all the flowers gone ?
  Girls have picked them, every one.
      When will they ever learn ?
      When will they ever learn ?

2   Where have all the young girls gone ?
      Long time passing.
  Where have all the young girls gone ?
      Long time ago.
  Where have all the young girls gone ?
  Taken husbands, every one.
      When will they ever learn ?
      When will they ever learn ?

3   Where have all the young men gone ? . . .
  Gone to soldiers, every one.

4   Where have all the soldiers gone ? . . .
  Gone to graveyards, every one.

5   Where have all the graveyards gone ? . . .
  Gone to flowers, every one.

6   Where have all the flowers gone ?

Pete Seeger

38 With a little help from my friends

1   What would you do if I sang out of tune,
      Would you stand up and walk out on me?
      Lend me your ears and I'll sing you a song,
      And I'll try not to sing out of key.

      Oh, I get by with a little help from my friends,
      Mm, I get high with a little help from my friends,
      Mm, I'm gonna try with a little help from my friends.

          Do you need anybody?
          I need somebody to love.
          Could it be anybody?
          I want somebody to love.

2   What do I do when my love is away?
      Does it worry you to be alone?
      How do I feel by the end of the day?
      Are you sad because you're on your own?

      No, I get by with a little help from my friends,
      Mm, I get high with a little help from my friends,
      Mm, I'm gonna try with a little help from my friends.

          Do you need anybody?
          I just need someone to love.
          Could it be anybody?
          I want somebody to love.

3   Would you believe in a love at first sight ?
    Yes, I'm certain that it happens all the time.
    What do you see when you turn out the light ?
    I can't tell you, but I know it's mine.

    Oh, I get by with a little help from my friends,
    Mm, I get high with a little help from my friends,
    Oh, I'm gonna try with a little help from my friends,
    Yes, I get by with a little help from my friends,
        with a little help from my friends.

John Lennon and Paul McCartney

39 Moving on song

1   Born in the middle of the afternoon
     In a horse-drawn wagon on the old A5,
     The big twelve-wheelers shook me bed,
     "You can't stop here!" the policeman said,
     "You'd better get born in some place else."

       So move along! Get along!
       Move along! Get along!
       Go! Move! Shift!

2   Born in the tattie-lifting time
     In an auld bow-tent near a tattie field;
     The farmer said, "The work's all done,
     It's time that you was moving on,
     You'd better get born in some place else."

3   Born on a common near a building site,
     Where the ground is rutted by the trailer's wheels;
     The local people said to me:
     "You'll lower the price of property,
     You'd better get born in some place else."

4 Born at the back of a blackthorn hedge,
   When the white hoar-frost lay all around;
   No eastern kings came bearing gifts,
   Instead, the order came to shift!
   You'd better get born in some place else.

5 The winter sky was hung with stars
   And one shone brighter than the rest;
   The wise men came, so stern and strict,
   And brought the order to evict,
   You'd better get born in some place else.

6 Wagon, tent or trailer-born,
   Last month, last year or in far-off days,
   Born here or a thousand miles away,
   There's always men nearby who say:
   "You'd better get born in some place else."

Ewan MacColl

40 Mr Tambourine Man

Hey! Mr Tambourine Man, play a song for me,
I'm not sleepy and there is no place I'm goin' to.
Hey! Mr Tambourine Man, play a song for me,
In the jingle jangle mornin' I'll come followin' you.

1 Though I know that evenin's empire has returned
        into sand,
            Vanished from my hand,
    Left me blindly here to stand but still not sleepin'!
    My weariness amazes me, I'm branded on my feet.
            I have no one to meet,
    And the ancient empty street's too dead for dreamin'.
            Hey! Mr Tambourine Man . . .

2 Take me on a trip upon your magic swirlin' ship,
            My senses have been stripped,
            My hands can't feel to grip,
            My toes too numb to step,
    Wait only for my boot heels to be wanderin'.
    I'm ready to go anywhere, I'm ready for to fade
            Into my own parade,
            Cast your dancin' spell my way,
    I promise to go under it.
            Hey! Mr Tambourine Man . . .

3   Though you might hear laughin', spinnin', swingin'
          madly across the sun,
       It's not aimed at anyone,
       It's just escapin' on the run,
   And but for the sky there are no fences facin'.
   And if you hear vague traces of skippin' reels of rhyme
       To your tambourine in time,
       It's just a ragged clown behind,
       I wouldn't pay it any mind,
   It's just a shadow you're seein' that he's chasin'.
       Hey! Mr Tambourine Man . . .

4   Then take me disappearin' through the smoke rings of
          my mind,
       Down the foggy ruins of time,
       Far past the frozen leaves,
       The haunted, frightened trees,
       Out to the windy beach,
   Far from the twisted reach of crazy sorrow.
   Yes, to dance beneath the diamond sky with one hand
          wavin' free,
       Silhouetted by the sea,
       Circled by the circus sands,
       With all memory and fate
       Driven deep beneath the waves,
   Let me forget about today until tomorrow.
       Hey! Mr Tambourine Man . . .

Bob Dylan

41 Streets of London

1 Have you seen the old man in the closed-down market,
Kicking up the papers with his worn-out shoes?
In his eyes you see no pride, hand held loosely by
  his side,
Yesterday's paper telling yesterday's news.

So how can you tell me you're lonely
And say for you that the sun don't shine?
Let me take you by the hand and lead you through
  the streets of London.
I'll show you something to make you change your
  mind.

2 In the all-night café at a quarter past eleven,
Same old man sitting there on his own,
Looking at the world over the rim of his teacup.
Each tea lasts an hour and he wanders home alone.

3 Have you seen the old girl who walks the streets of
  London,
Dirt in her hair and her clothes in rags?
She's no time for talkin', she just keeps on walkin',
Carrying her home in two carrier-bags.

4 Have you seen the old man outside the Seaman's
  Mission,
Memory fading with the medals that he wears?
In our winter city the rain cries a little pity
For one forgotten hero and a world that doesn't care.

Ralph McTell

42 Let there be peace on earth

1   Let there be peace on earth
    And let it begin with me;
    Let there be peace on earth,
    The peace that was meant to be.
        With God as our Father,
        Brothers all are we.
        Let me walk with my brother
        In perfect harmony.

2   Let peace begin with me,
    Let this be the moment now.
    With every step I take,
    Let this be my solemn vow:
        To take each moment and live each moment
        In peace eternally.
        Let there be peace on earth
        And let it begin with me.

Sing the song through twice

Sy Miller and Jill Jackson

43 Make me a channel of your peace

1   Make me a channel of your peace.
    Where there is hatred, let me bring your love.
    Where there is injury, your pardon, Lord.
    And where there's doubt, true faith in you.

2   Make me a channel of your peace.
    Where there's despair in life, let me bring hope.
    Where there is darkness, only light.
    And where there's sadness, ever joy.

3   Oh, Master, grant that I may never seek
    So much to be consoled as to console,
    To be understood as to understand,
    To be loved, as to love, with all my soul.

4   Make me a channel of your peace.
    It is in pardoning that we are pardoned,
    In giving to all men that we receive,
    And in dying that we're born to eternal life.

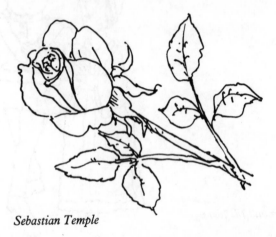

Sebastian Temple

44 A rose is sweet

1 Bring me a rose in the wintertime,
When it's hard to find,
Bring me a rose in the wintertime,
I have roses on my mind.
> A rose is sweet most anytime and yet,
> Bring me a rose in the wintertime,
> How easily we forget!

2 Bring me the truth in the wintertime,
When it's hard to find,
Bring me the truth in the wintertime,
I have truth on my mind.
> The truth is sweet in the face of lies,
> Bring me the truth in the wintertime,
> How easily we forget!

3 Bring me love in the wintertime,
When it's hard to find,
Bring me love in the wintertime,
I have loving on my mind.
> For love is sweet where hate abounds,
> Bring me some love in the wintertime,
> I have loving on my mind.

4 Bring me peace in the wintertime,
When it's hard to find,
Bring me peace in the wintertime,
I have peace on my mind.
> For peace is sweet when there's talk of war,
> Bring us peace in the wintertime,
> I have peace on my mind.

Traditional

45 Last night I had the strangest dream

1 Last night I had the strangest dream
   I ever dreamed before.
   I dreamed the world had all agreed
   To put an end to war.

2 I dreamed I saw a mighty room,
   And the room was filled with men,
   And the paper they were signing said
   They'd never fight again.

3 And when the paper was all signed
   And a million copies made,
   They all joined hands and bowed their heads,
   And graceful prayers were made.

4 And the people in the streets below
   Were dancing round and round,
   Whilst swords and guns and uniforms
   Were scattered on the ground.

5 Last night I had the strangest dream
   I ever dreamed before.
   I dreamed the world had all agreed
   To put an end to war.

Ed McCurdy

46 Peace will soon come to be

I look around, loving
All of the joys I see.
I close my eyes, praying
Peace will soon come to be.

1 Sun on the sea,
  Waves on the shore,
  But in another land,
  Guns and bullets roar.
      I look around . . .

2 Wind in my hair,
  Rain on my face,
  But in another land,
  People hope for peace.
      I look around . . .

3 Dew on the grass,
  Flowers that grow,
  But in another land,
  Blood and tears flow.
      I look around . . .

Chris and John Hoggarth

47 Agada

1   Al sfat yam kineret
    Armon rav tiferet,
    Gan el sham natua,
    Bo etz lo yanua.

2   Mi gar sham, rak naar
    Keof bidemi yaar;
    Lomed sham tora hu
    Mipi mipi eliyahu.

3   Hass gal lo koleach.
    Kol of haporeach
    Omed veshomea,
    Torat el bolea.

Yaakov Fichman

1 On the shores of Lake Kineret
   There is a most glorious palace,
   A garden of God is planted there,
   In which no tree moves.

2 A boy dwells there, like a bird
   In the silence of the forest.
   There he learns the Torah
   From the mouth of Eliyahu.

3 Hush! Not a wave spouts.
   Every bird that flies
   Stands and listens,
   Absorbing God's Torah.

48 Peace is flowing like a river

1 Peace is flowing like a river,
   Flowing out through you and me,
   Spreading out into the desert,
   Setting all the captives free.

2 Love is flowing . . .

3 Joy is flowing . . .

4 Hope is flowing . . .

Traditional

49 Hévénu shalōm

Hévénu shalōm aléchem,
Hévénu shalōm aléchem,
Hévénu shalōm aléchem,
Hévénu shalōm, shalōm, shalōm aléchem.

Peace unto you!

Traditional

50 Put your hand in the hand

1 Put your hand in the hand of the man
    who stilled the water.
  Put your hand in the hand of the man
    who calmed the sea.
  Take a look at yourself and you can look
    at others differently,
  By puttin' your hand in the hand of the man
    from Galilee.

2 Every time I look into the Holy Book
    I want to tremble.
  When I read about the part where a carpenter
    cleared the temple.
  For the buyers and the sellers were no different
    fellas than what I profess to be,
  And it causes me pain to know we're not the people
    we should be.

3   Put your hand in the hand of the man
          who stilled the water.
    Put your hand in the hand of the man
          who calmed the sea.
    Take a look at yourself and you can look
          at others differently,
    By puttin' your hand in the hand of the man
          from Galilee.

Gene MacLellan

51 It's me, O Lord

It's me, it's me, it's me, O Lord,
Standin' in the need of prayer.
It's me, it's me, it's me, O Lord,
Standin' in the need of prayer.

1   Not my brother or my sister, but it's me, O Lord,
    Standin' in the need of prayer.
    Not my brother or my sister, but it's me, O Lord,
    Standin' in the need of prayer.
        It's me, it's me . . .

2   Not my mother or my father . . .

3   Not the stranger or my neighbour . . .

Spiritual

52 *Temptation*

1   Temptation, get away from me,
       Temptation, get away from me,
             I mean to shine like a little star
             Away up there where the good souls are,
             Get away from me –
             But not too far.

2   Temptation, get away from me,
       Temptation, get away from me,
             This wordly sea is tempest tossed,
             I know that Jordan must be crossed,
             Get away from me –
             But don't get lost.

3   Temptation, get away from me,
       Temptation, get away from me,
             I've listened to your siren song,
             I've learned to know the right from wrong,
             Get away from me –
             But don't be long.

Malvina Reynolds

53 Sinner man

O sinner man, where will you run to?
O sinner man, where will you run to?
O sinner man, where will you run to,
All on that day?

1 Run to the rocks, rocks won't you hide me?
   Run to the rocks, rocks won't you hide me?
   Run to the rocks, rocks won't you hide me,
   All on that day?
       O sinner man . . .

2 Run to the sea, sea is a-boiling . . .

3 Run to the Lord, Lord won't you hide me? . . .

4 O sinner man, should bin a-praying . . .

Spiritual

54 Somebody got lost in a storm

1 Somebody got lost in a storm,
   Somebody got lost in a storm,
   Somebody got lost, somebody got lost,
   Somebody got lost in a storm.

2 Poor sinner got lost in a storm . . .

3 Somebody got lost in a storm . . .

4 Don't ever get lost in a storm . . .

5 Somebody got lost in a storm . . .

Spiritual

55 You've got to walk that lonesome valley

1 You've got to walk that lonesome valley,
   You've got to walk there by yourself;
   And no one here can walk there for you,
   You've got to walk there by yourself.

2 You've got to face one day your Maker,
   You've got to face him by yourself;
   And no one here can face him for you,
   You've got to face him by yourself.

3 You've got to stand one day in Judgement,
   You've got to stand there by yourself;
   And no one here can stand there for you,
   You've got to stand there by yourself.

4 You've got to walk that lonesome valley,
   You've got to walk there by yourself;
   And no one here can walk there for you,
   You've got to walk there by yourself.

Traditional

56 The fields are white

1 The fields are white unto harvest time,
   Look up and see!
   The fields are white unto harvest time,
   Look up and see:

   Pray to the Lord of the harvest,
   Christ says pray.
   Pray to the Lord for the workers
   Which we need in this day.

2 The harvest truly is fit to reap
   But workers few,
   The harvest truly is fit to reap
   But workers few:

3 Who else will 'go into all the world'
   To preach the Word?
   Who else will 'go into all the world'
   To preach the Word?

4 The Lord's return may be very soon,
   The time is short!
   The Lord's return may be very soon,
   The time is short:

M. A. Baughen

57 Children go, I will send you

1   Children go, I will send you.
How will you send me?
Oh, I will send you one by one,
One for the little bitty baby boy
Born, born in Bethlehem, Bethlehem, Bethlehem.

2   Children go, I will send you.
How will you send me?
Oh, I will send you two by two,
Two for Joseph and Mary,
One for the little bitty baby boy
Born, born in Bethlehem, Bethlehem, Bethlehem.

3   Three for the good old wise men . . .

4   Four for the oxen that stood in the stall . . .

5   Five for the snow that lay on the ground . . .

6   Children go, I will send you.
How will you send me?
Oh, I will send you six by six,
Six for the stars that shone in the sky,
Five for the snow that lay on the ground,
Four for the oxen that stood in the stall,
Three for the good old wise men,
Two for Joseph and Mary,
One for the little bitty baby boy
Born, born in Bethlehem, Bethlehem, Bethlehem.

Traditional

58 Raindrops keep fallin' on my head

Raindrops keep fallin' on my head,
And just like the guy whose feet are too big
    for his bed,
Nothin' seems to fit.
Those raindrops are fallin' on my head,
They keep fallin'!

So I just did me some talkin' to the sun,
And I said I didn't like the way he got things done;
Sleepin' on the job.
Those raindrops are fallin' on my head,
They keep fallin'!

    But there's one thing I know,
    The blues they send to meet me
    Won't defeat me.
    It won't be long till happiness
    Steps up to greet me.

Raindrops keep fallin' on my head,
But that doesn't mean my eyes will soon be
    turnin' red;
Cryin's not for me,
'Cause I'm never gonna stop the rain by complainin'.
Because I'm free – nothin's worryin' me.

Hal David

59 The building song

1 All over the world,
   Everywhere,
   Where the sun shines,
   And where the white snow gleams;
   In the green, green forests and by the streams,
   Hands are busy,
   Plans are laid,
   And slowly, slowly,
   Somewhere, somebody's house is made.

       Everybody's building, everybody's building,
       Everybody's building day by day,
       Everybody's building, everybody's building,
       Everybody's building in a different way.

2 All over the world,
   Everywhere,
   Where the sun shines,
   And where the darkest night
   Holds back the coming of the morning light:
   Bricks are laid and wood is sawn,
   And slowly, slowly,
   Out of a dream a house is born.

3 All over the world,
  Everywhere,
  Where we're living,
  Wherever children grow,
  And their lives are shaped as the moments go,
  Minds are building, plans are laid,
  And slowly, slowly,
  Somewhere, somebody's life is made.

4 All over the world,
  Everywhere,
  Where we're living,
  Wherever children play,
  By the things they do and the things they say,
  For good or ill, ground is laid,
  And slowly, slowly,
  Somewhere, somebody's life is made.

David Winter

60 *A better world*

Wake up each day,
Sun shining through,
Showing the way to
A better world for you.
Wake up each day,
Sun shining through,
Showing the way to
A better world for you.

1   Morning is the time,
    Make each day seem fine.
    In all you do, just try a smile –
    Makes each task seem so worth while.
    Friendships every day
    Help you on your way.
    They give you strength when you are down,
    Bring you smiles to ease your frown.
        Wake up each day . . .

2   Every girl and boy,
    Fill each day with joy,
    Helpful hands and gentle ways
    In our work and in our play.
    Then when day is through,
    Look back on all you do.
    Have you given of your best ?
    Happy hearts will win the test.
        Wake up each day . . .

Chris and John Hoggarth

61 One man's hands

1   One man's hands can't break a prison down,
    Two men's hands can't break a prison down,
    But if two and two and fifty make a million,
    We'll see that day come round,
    We'll see that day come round.

2   One man's voice can't shout to make them hear,
    Two men's voices can't shout to make them hear,
    But if two and two and fifty make a million,
    We'll see that day come round,
    We'll see that day come round.

3   One man's strength can't ban the atom bomb . . .

4   One man's eyes can't see the way ahead . . .

Alex Comfort

62 Oh, Mary, don't you weep

Oh, Mary, don't you weep, don't you mourn,
Oh, Mary, don't you weep, don't you mourn.
Pharaoh's army got drownded;
Oh, Mary, don't you weep.

1   If I could, I surely would
Stand on the rock where Moses stood.
Pharoah's army got drownded;
Oh, Mary, don't you weep.
     Oh, Mary, don't you weep . . .

2   Some of these nights about twelve o'clock,
This old world's going to reel and rock.
Pharaoh's army got drownded;
Oh, Mary, don't you weep.
     Oh, Mary, don't you weep . . .

Spiritual

63 All my trials

1   Hush, little baby, don't you cry,
    You know your Mamma was born to die.
        All my trials, Lord, soon be over.

2   I have a little book with pages three,
    And every page spells liberty.
        All my trials, Lord, soon be over.

        Too late, my brothers,
        Too late, but never mind;
        All my trials, Lord, soon be over.

3   If living were a thing that money could buy,
    The rich would live and the poor would die.
        All my trials, Lord, soon be over.

4   There grows a tree in Paradise
    And the pilgrims call it the Tree of Life.
        All my trials, Lord, soon be over.

        Too late, my brothers,
        Too late, but never mind;
        All my trials, Lord, soon be over.

Spiritual

64 Donna, donna

1   On a wagon bound for market
   Lies a calf with a mournful eye;
   High above him flies a swallow,
   Winging freely through the sky.

     How the winds are laughing!
     They laugh with all their might;
     Laugh and laugh the whole day through
     And half the summer's night.
     Donna, donna, donna, donna,
     Donna, donna, donna, don.
     Donna, donna, donna, donna,
     Donna, donna, donna, don.

2   "Stop complaining!" said the farmer,
   "Who told you a calf to be?
   Why don't you have wings to fly with,
   Like that swallow proud and free?"
     How the winds are laughing . . .

3   Calves are easily bound and slaughtered,
   Never knowing the reason why,
   But whoever treasures freedom,
   Like that swallow learns to fly.
     How the winds are laughing . . .

*Sheldon Secunda, Aaron Zeitlin, Arthur Kevess
and Teddi Schwartz*

65 Ush'avtem mayim

Ush'avtem mayim b'sason
Mimainé hay'shua,
Ush'avtem mayim b'sason
Mimainé hay'shua,
Mayim, mayim, mayim, mayim,
Ho mayim b'sason
Mayim, mayim, mayim, mayim,
Ho mayim b'sason
Hey, hey, hey, hey,
Mayim, mayim, mayim, mayim,
Mayim, mayim, b'sason
Mayim, mayim, mayim, mayim,
Mayim, mayim b'sason.

Joyfully shall you draw upon the fountains
    of deliverance.

Isaiah 12, v.3

66 Sing a song of freedom

1   As I look around me,
      I see the world in a different light;
  Everything is changing
      and it happened overnight.
  Changing for the better
      and it starts with you and me,
  So we'll sing our song together
      and for ever we'll be free.

      Sing a song of freedom,
      Everyone join in.
      People come together,
      Everybody sing.
      Sing a song of freedom,
      Each and every man.
      People come together,
      All across the land.

2   If you're looking for an answer,
      it's very close at hand.
  Just take a look around you
      and then you'll understand.
  Clap your hands together
      and let me hear the sound.
  It's the time for liberation,
      so pass the word around.

Guy Fletcher and Doug Flett

67 Live, live, live

Live, live, live,
Live, live, live.
Jesus is living in my soul.
Live, live, live,
Live, live, live.
Jesus is living in my soul.

1   Hanging on the tree,
    He prayed for you and me.
            Jesus is living in my soul.
    To the spirit yield,
    By his stripes we're healed.
            Jesus is living in my soul.
            Live, live, live . . .

2   He took me out of darkness,
    And he set me free.
            Jesus is living in my soul.
    Once I was blind,
    Now I can see.
            Jesus is living in my soul.
            Live, live, live . . .

3   Gonna shout and sing,
    Let the hallelujah ring.
            Jesus is living in my soul.
    I'm gonna shout and sing,
    There's healing in his wing.
            Jesus is living in my soul.
            Live, live, live . . .

Marcus Uzilevsky

68 By the waters of Babylon

1   By the waters, the waters of Babylon,
     We sat down and wept, and wept for thee, Zion;
     We remember thee, remember thee, remember
        thee, Zion.

2   On the willows, the willows of Babylon,
     We hung up our harps, our harps for thee, Zion;
     How can we sing, can we sing, sing of thee, Zion?

3   There our captors, our captors from Babylon,
     Tried to make us sing, and sing of thee, Zion;
     But we could not sing, we could not sing, we
        could not sing, Zion.

Based on Psalm 137

69 Wade in the water

Wade in the water,
Wade in the water, children,
Wade in the water,
God's gonna trouble these waters.

1 See that band all dressed in white,
      God's gonna trouble these waters,
   Look like a band of the Israelites,
      God's gonna trouble these waters.
      Wade in the water . . .

2 See that band all dressed in red,
      God's gonna trouble these waters,
   Look like a band that Moses led,
      God's gonna trouble these waters.
      Wade in the water . . .

Spiritual

70 Joshua fit the battle of Jericho

Joshua fit the battle of Jericho, Jericho,
    Jericho,
Joshua fit the battle of Jericho,
And the walls came tumbling down.

1   You may talk about your king of Gideon,
    You may.talk about your man of Saul,
    But there's none like good old Joshua
    At the battle of Jericho.

2   Up to the walls of Jericho
    He marched with spear in hand.
    "Go blow them ram-horns," Joshua cried,
    "Cause the battle am in my hand."

3   Then the ram-sheeps' horns began to blow,
    Trumpets began to sound.
    Joshua commanded the children to shout,
    And the walls came tumbling down, that morning

Joshua fit the battle of Jericho, Jericho,
    Jericho,
Joshua fit the battle of Jericho,
And the walls came tumbling down.

Spiritual

71 The tramp on the street

1 Only a tramp was Lazarus that begged,
   He lay down by the rich man's gate,
   He begged for crumbs from the rich man to eat,
   But they left him to die like a tramp on the street.

2 He was somebody's darlin', he was some mother's son,
   Once he was fair, and once he was young,
   Some mother she rocked him, her little darlin' to sleep,
   But they left him to die like a tramp on the street.

3 Jesus who died on Calvary's Tree,
   Shed his life-blood for you and for me,
   They pierced his side, his hands and his feet
   And they left him to die like a tramp on the street.

4 He was Mary's own darlin', he was God's chosen son,
   Once he was fair, and once he was young,
   Mary she rocked him, her little darlin' to sleep,
   But they left him to die like a tramp on the street.

5 When the battles are over and the victory's won,
   Everyone mourns for the poor man's son,
   Red, White and Blue and victory's sweet,
   And they left him to die like a tramp on the street.

6 He was somebody's darlin', he was some mother's son,
   Once he was fair, and once he was young,
   Some mother she rocked him, her little darlin' to sleep,
   But they left him to die like a tramp on the street.

Grady and Hazel Cole

72 Oh, the Lord looked down

1   Oh, the Lord looked down from his window in the sky,
Said: "I created man, but I can't remember why!
Nothing but fighting since creation day.
I'll send a little water and wash them all away."
Oh, the Lord came down and looked around a spell.
There was Mr Noah behaving mighty well.
And that is the reason the Scriptures record
Noah found grace in the eyes of the Lord.

        Noah found grace in the eyes of the Lord,
        Noah found grace in the eyes of the Lord,
        Noah found grace in the eyes of the Lord
        And he left him high and dry.

2   The Lord said: "Noah, there's going to be a flood,
There's going to be some water, there's going to be
      some mud,
So, take off your hat, Noah, take off your coat,
Get Shem, Ham and Japheth and build yourself a
      boat."
Noah said: "Lord, I don't believe I could."
The Lord said: "Noah, get yourself some wood.
You never know what you can do till you try.
Build it fifty cubits wide and thirty cubits high."
      Noah found grace in the eyes of the Lord . . .

3   Noah said: "There she is, there she is, Lord!"
The Lord said: "Noah, it's time to get aboard.
Take of each creature a he and a she,
And of course take Mrs Noah and the whole family."
Noah said: "Lord, it's getting mighty dark."
The Lord said: "Noah, get those creatures in the ark."
Noah said: "Lord, it's beginning to pour."
The Lord said: "Noah, hurry up and close the door."
    Noah found grace . . .

4   The ark rose up on the bosom of the deep.
After forty days Mr Noah took a peep.
He said: "We're not moving, Lord, where are we at?"
The Lord said: "You're sitting right on Mount Ararat."
Noah said: "Lord, it's getting nice and dry."
The Lord said: "Noah, see my rainbow in the sky.
Take all your creatures and people the earth,
And be sure that you're not more trouble than you're
    worth."
    Noah found grace . . .

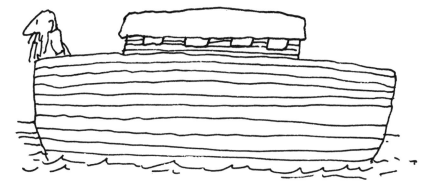

Traditional

73 Moses, I know you're the man

1 "Moses, I know you're the man,"
    The Lord said,
"You're going to work out my plan,"
    The Lord said,
"Lead all the Israelites out of slavery,
And I shall make them a wandering race
    Called the people of God."

        So every day we're on our way,
        For we're a travelling, wandering race:
        We're the people of God.

2 "Don't get too set in your ways,"
    The Lord said,
"Each step is only a phase,"
    The Lord said,
"I'll go before you and I shall be a sign
To guide my travelling, wandering race,
    You're the people of God."

3 "No matter what you may do,"
    The Lord said,
"I shall be faithful and true,"
    The Lord said,
"My love will strengthen you as you go along,
For you're my travelling, wandering race,
    You're the people of God."

4 "Look at the birds in the air,"
        The Lord said,
   "They fly unhampered by care,"
        The Lord said,
   "You will move easier if you're travelling light,
   For you're a wandering, vagabond race,
        You're the people of God."

5 "Foxes have places to go,"
        The Lord said,
   "But I've no home here below,"
        The Lord said,
   "So if you want to be with me all your days,
   Keep up the moving and travelling on,
        You're the people of God."

Estelle White

74 Rise and shine

Rise, and shine, and give God his glory, glory.
Rise, and shine, and give God his glory, glory.
Rise, and shine, and give God his glory, glory,
Children of the Lord.

1 The Lord said to Noah: "There's gonna be a floody,
    floody."
Lord said to Noah: "There's gonna be a floody,
    floody.
Get those children out of the muddy, muddy,"
Children of the Lord.
    Rise, and shine . . .

2 So Noah, he built him, he built him an arky, arky.
Noah, he built him, he built him an arky, arky.
Built it out of hickory barky, barky,
Children of the Lord.
    Rise, and shine . . .

3 The animals, they came on, they came on by twosies,
    twosies,
The animals, they came on, they came on by twosies,
    twosies,
Elephants and kangaroosies, roosies,
Children of the Lord.
    Rise, and shine . . .

4   It rained and poured for forty daysies, daysies,
    It rained and poured for forty daysies, daysies,
    Nearly drove those animals crazyies, crazyies,
    Children of the Lord.
         Rise, and shine . . .

5   The sun came out and dried up the landy, landy,
    The sun came out and dried up the landy, landy,
    Everything was fine and dandy, dandy,
    Children of the Lord.
         Rise, and shine . . .

6   If you get to heaven before I dosies, dosies,
    If you get to heaven before I dosies, dosies,
    Tell those angels, I'm comin' toosies, toosies,
    Children of the Lord.
         Rise, and shine . . .

Traditional

75 All night, all day

All night, all day,
    Angels watchin' over me, my Lord.
All night, all day,
    Angels watchin' over me.

1   Day is dyin' in the west,
    Angels watchin' over me, my Lord.
Sleep, my child, and take your rest,
    Angels watchin' over me.
    All night, all day . . .

2   Now I lay me down to sleep,
    Angels watchin' over me, my Lord.
Pray the Lord my soul to keep,
    Angels watchin' over me.
    All night, all day . . .

Spiritual

76 Shalōm

Shalōm, my friend, shalōm, my friend,
    Shalōm, shalōm.
Till we meet again, till we meet again,
    Shalōm, shalōm.

Traditional

77 *Amen*

Amen, amen,
Amen, amen, amen.

1 See the baby
   Lying in a manger
   One Christmas morning.
       Amen, amen . . .

2 See him in the temple
   Talking to the elders,
   Boy with head so wise.
       Amen, amen . . .

3 See him at the seaside
   Healing and a-preaching
   To the poor and sick.
       Amen, amen . . .

4 See him in the garden
   Praying to the Father,
   Deep in his sorrow.
       Amen, amen . . .

5 Jesus was born,
   Born to die for all men;
   Now he lives again.
       Amen, amen . . .

Spiritual

Acknowledgements

Grateful acknowledgement is made to the following who have granted permission for the reprinting of copyright material:

Alpha Music, Inc. for 67 – 'Live, live, live' (Uzilevsky) ©1974 Oaksprings Workshop ©1980 assigned to Alpha Music, Inc. All rights reserved. Used by permission.

April Music for 19 – 'Music of the world a-turnin' ' (Levitt/Thomas) © 1965 Blackwood Music Inc.

Ardmore & Beechwood Ltd and International Music Publications for 50 – 'Put your hand in the hand' (MacLellan) © 1970 Beechwood Music, Canada

ATV Music Ltd for 20 – 'Nowhere Man' (Lennon/McCartney) © 1965 Northern Songs for the World and 38 – 'With a little help from my friends' (Lennon/McCartney) © 1967 Northern Songs for the World

The Rev. Michael A. Baughen for 56 – 'The fields are white' © 1964 M. A. Baughen

Columbia Pictures Publications and International Music Publications for 5 – 'Happiness is' (Parnes/Erans) © 1965 Mills Music Inc. and 64 – 'Donna, donna' (Secunda/Zeitlin/Kevess/Schwartz) © 1940 Mills Music Inc.

Big Secret Music Ltd for 66 – 'Sing a song of freedom' (Fletcher/Flett) © 1971 Big Secret Music Ltd

Bogle-L'Ouverture Publications Ltd for 24 – 'Rain and sun' (Thomas) from *Rain Falling, Sun Shining* © 1975 Bogle-L'Ouverture Publications Ltd

Cambridge University Press for 11 – 'Guantanamera' (Brace) from *35 Songs from 35 Countries* compiled by Geoffrey Brace

Chappell Music Ltd and International Music Publications for 59 – 'The building song' (Winter) © 1972 Bradbury Wood Ltd and Chappell Music Ltd for the World

Dixie Music Publishing Co. for 71 – 'The tramp on the street' (Cole) © 1940 and 1947 Dixie Music Publishing Co.

Essex Music International Ltd for 33 – 'From both sides now' (Mitchell) © 1967 and 1972 Siquomb Publishing Corp., New York and 41 – 'Streets of London' (McTell) © 1968 and 1972 Essex Music International Ltd

Robert J. Figures for 6 – 'Alleluya'

Brian Fitzgerald for 36 – 'Where have the seals gone ?' (A Few Questions) © 1976 Brian Fitzgerald. First published in *Sounds Great 6* by the Education Department of Victoria, Australia

Franciscan Communications Centre for 43 – 'Make me a channel of your peace' (Temple) © Franciscan Communications Centre, Los Angeles, CA

Fred Bock Music Co. for 1 – 'Hey, now, everybody sing !' (Johnson) © 1961 Gentry Publications. All rights reserved.

MCA Music Ltd for 58 – 'Raindrops keep fallin' on my head' (David) © 1969 Blue Seas Music Ltd, Jac Music Co. Ltd and Twentieth Century Music Corp. Ltd

Harmony Music Ltd for 13 – 'Lullaby for the times' (MacColl) © 1962 Stormking Music Inc., New York; 34 – 'Can't help but wonder' (Paxton) © 1963 Cherry Lane Music Inc., New York; 37 – 'Where have all the flowers gone ?' (Seeger) © 1961 Fall River Music Inc., New York; 39 – 'Moving on song' (MacColl) © 1964 Stormking Music Inc., New York; 61 – 'One man's hands' (Comfort) © 1962 Fall River Music Inc., New York

Chris and John Hoggarth for 46 – 'Peace will soon come to be' © 1979 Chris and John Hoggarth and 60 – 'A better world' © 1979 Chris and John Hoggarth

Jan-Lee Music for 42 – 'Let there be peace on earth' (Jackson/Miller) © 1955 Jan-Lee Music. Used by permission.

Kensington Music Ltd for 45 – 'Last night I had the strangest dream' (McCurdy)

Kevin Mayhew Publishers for 8 – 'Praise to the Lord our God' (White) from *20th Century Folk Hymnal Vol. 1* and 15 – 'I watch the sunrise' (Glynn) from *20th Century Folk Hymnal Vol 2* published by Kevin Mayhew Ltd, 55 Leigh Road, Leigh on Sea, Essex

Leeds Music Ltd, London, Leeds Music (Canada) and Leeds Music Pty Ltd, Australia for 10 – 'Magic Penny' (Reynolds) © 1955 Northern Music Co., U.S.A. © Leeds Music Ltd, 138 Piccadilly, London W1V 9FH © Leeds Music Pty Ltd for Australasia and New Zealand

Lowery Chappell Music and International Music Publications for 21 – 'The games people play' (South) © 1968 Lowery Music Co. Inc.

Mayhew-McCrimmon Ltd for 17 – 'Love is his word' (Connaughton) and 73 – 'Moses, I know you're the man' (White)

Leon Rosselson for 23 – 'Bus story' © 1974 Leon Rosselson

Salvationist Publishing and Supplies Ltd for 26 – 'Silver trumpet' from *Songs for Joy* © 1970 Salvationist Publishing and Supplies Ltd. Used by permission of the International Music Board of The Salvation Army

Schroder Music Co. for 52 – 'Temptation' (Reynolds) © 1965 Schroder Music Co. (ASCAP) (U.S.A.). Used by permission

Songs and Creations for 12 – 'Forever free' (Anderson) © 1972 Songs and Creations and 16 – 'Abundantly' (Anderson) © 1968 Songs and Creations

TRO-Essex Music Ltd for 22 – 'Little boxes' (Reynolds) © 1963 Schroder Music Co.; 32 – 'Turn, turn, turn' (Seeger) © 1962 Melody Trails Inc., New York; 35 – 'What have they done to the rain ?' (Reynolds) © 1962 Schroder Music Co.

Vanguard Music Corporation, 250 W. 57th St., New York, N.Y. 10019 for 2 – 'God loves a cheerful giver' (Winter) © 1966 Medical Mission Sisters, Phil., Pa. Used by permission. Further reproduction prohibited.

Warner Bros. Music Ltd and International Music Publications for 31 – 'Blowin' in the wind' (Dylan) © 1962 and 1963 M. Witmark & Sons, New York and 40 – 'Mr Tambourine Man' (Dylan) © 1964 and 1965 M. Witmark & Sons, New York

The publishers are grateful to the Jewish National Fund for supplying 18 – 'Kol dŏdi,' 47 – 'Agada', 49 – 'Hévénu Shalŏm' and 65 – 'Ush'avtem mayim'.

Every effort has been made to trace and acknowledge copyright owners. If any right has been omitted, the publishers offer their apologies and will rectify this in subsequent editions following notification.

Index of first lines